Wise Publications
London/New York/Sydney/Paris

Exclusive Distributors:
Music Sales Limited
8/9 Frith Street,
London W1V 5TZ, England.
Music Sales Pty Limited
120 Rothschild Avenue,
Rosebery, NSW 2018,
Australia.

Order No.NO90540
ISBN 0-7119-3264-6

Music arranged by Frank Booth
Music processed by MSS Studios
Book design by Pearce Marchbank Studio
Computer origination by Adam Hay

Printed in the United Kingdom by
Halstan & Co Limited, Amersham, Buckinghamshire.

DRIVE MY CAR 4
NORWEGIAN WOOD 12
YOU WON'T SEE ME 8
NOWHERE MAN 15
THINK FOR YOURSELF 18
THE WORD 21
MICHELLE 24
WHAT GOES ON 28
GIRL 33
I'M LOOKING THROUGH YOU 36
IN MY LIFE 40
WAIT 46
IF I NEEDED SOMEONE 43
RUN FOR YOUR LIFE 50

DRIVE MY CAR

Words & Music by John Lennon & Paul McCartney.

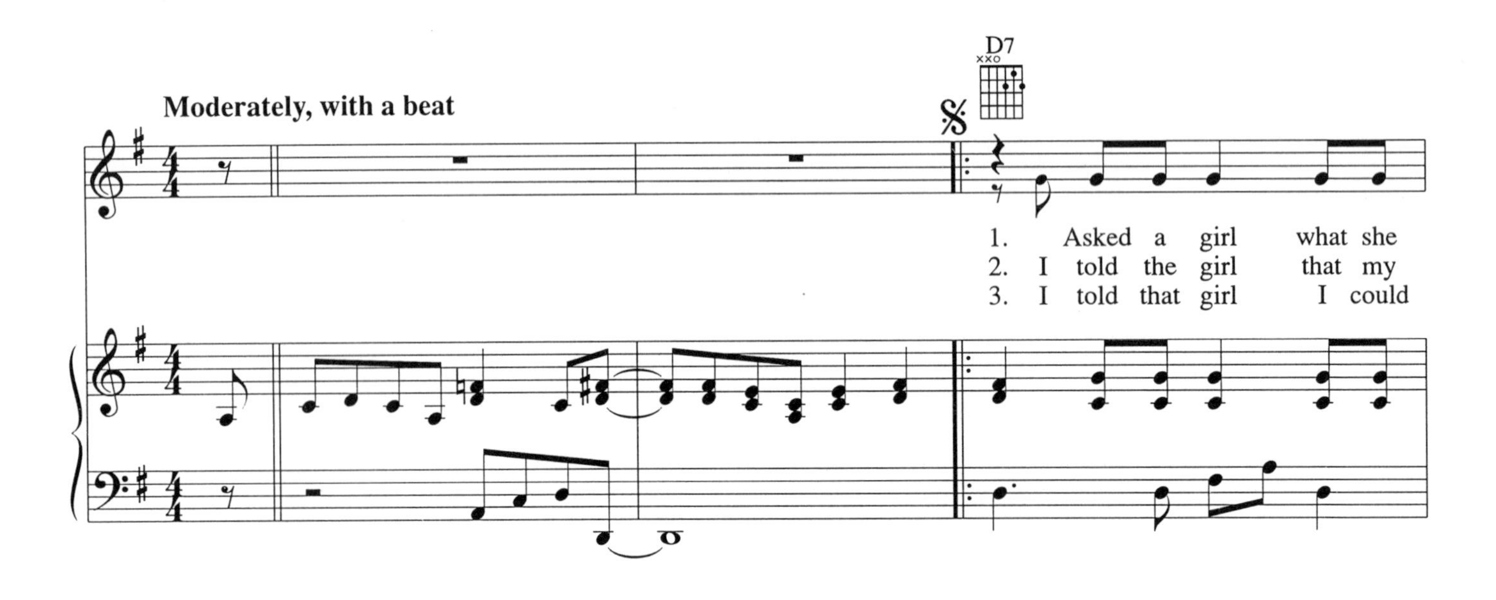

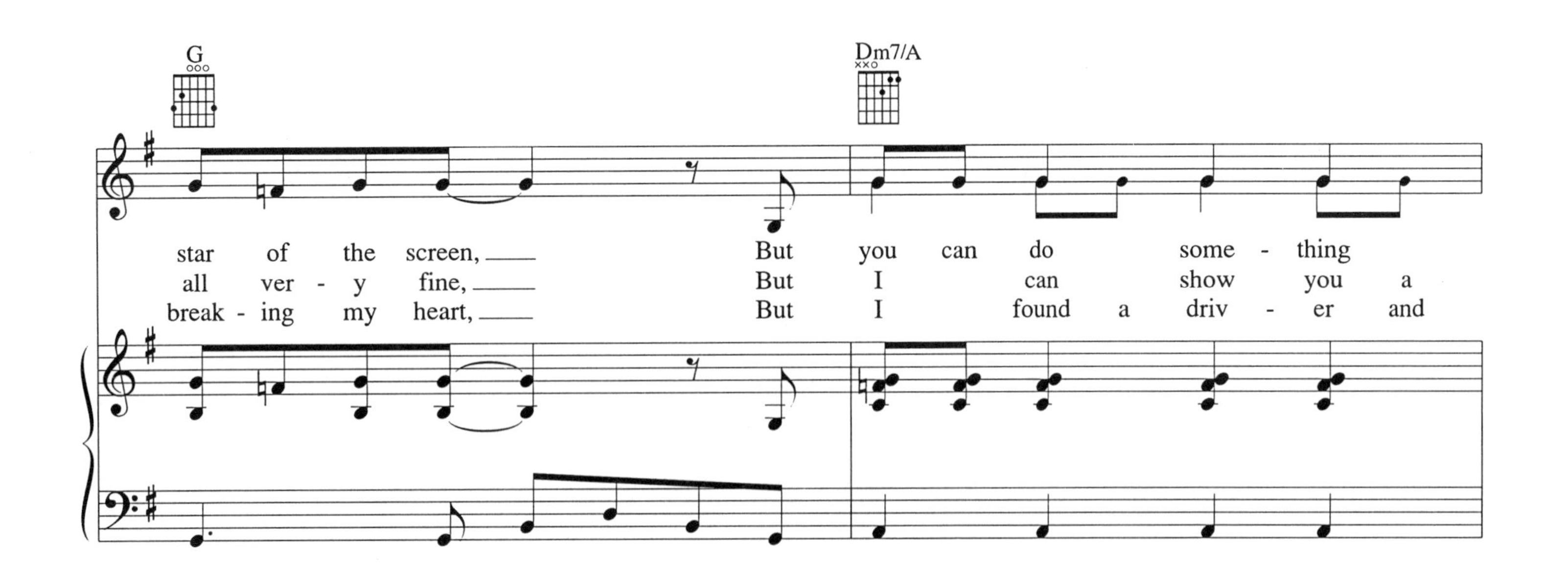
G
Dm7/A
star of the screen,
all ver - y fine,
break - ing my heart,
But you can do some - thing
But I can show you a
But I found a driv - er and

Bm
G7
in be - tween."
bet - ter time."
that's a start."
"Ba - by, you can drive my car,

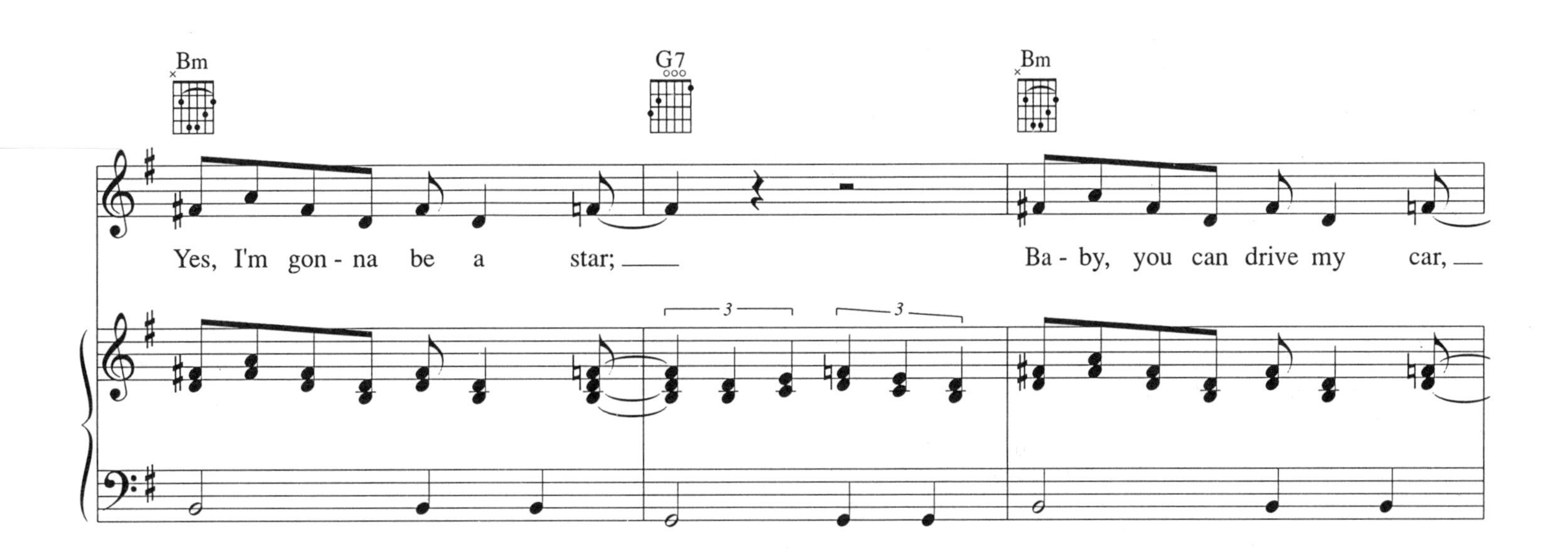
Bm
G7
Bm
Yes, I'm gon - na be a star;
Ba - by, you can drive my car,

E7♭9
Am
To Coda
D
G
1
A
and may - be I'll love you."
2
A
Tacet
D7
G
Beep, beep, mm beep, beep. Yeah.
D7
G
D7
G
Dm7/A

Bm
G7
Bm
"Ba - by, you can drive my car,
Yes, I'm gon - na be a star;
G7
Bm
E7♭9
Am
To Coda
Ba - by, you can drive my car,
and may - be I'll love
D
G
A
D.S. al Coda
(verse 3)
you."
Coda
D
G
you."
A
D
G
Repeat and Fade
Beep, beep, mm beep beep. Yeah.

YOU WON'T SEE ME

Words & Music by John Lennon & Paul McCartney.

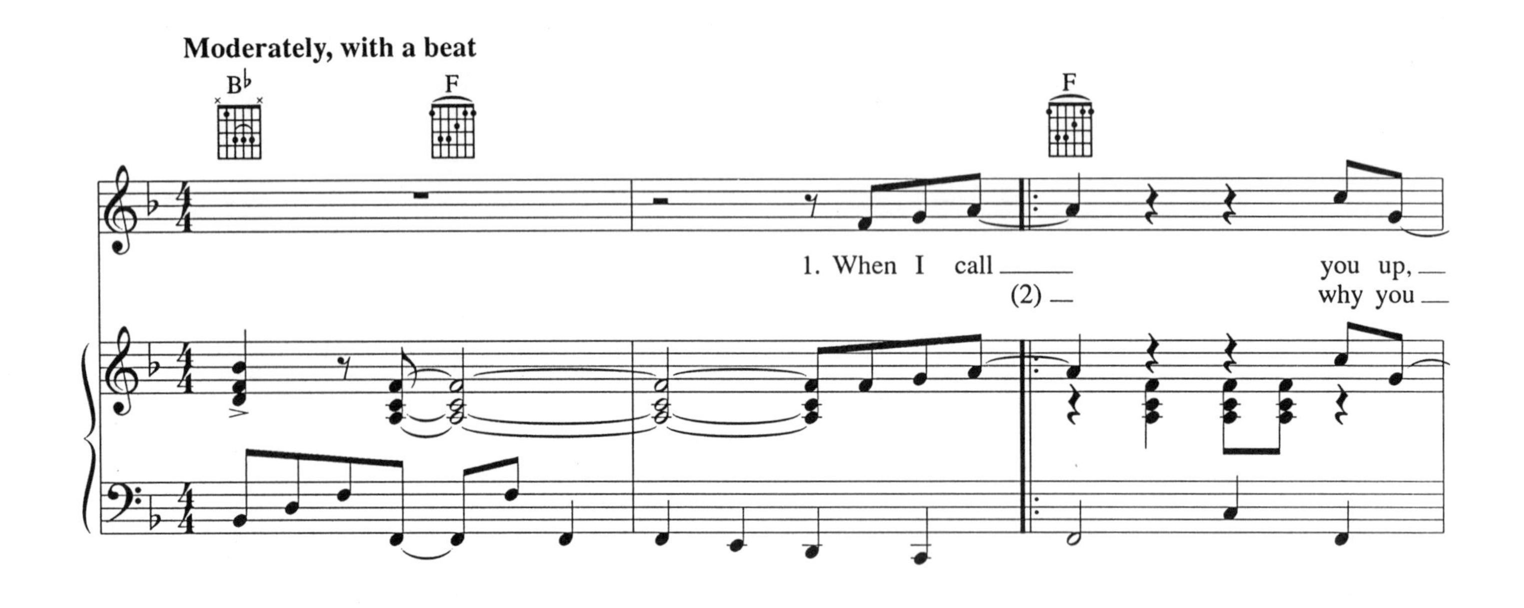

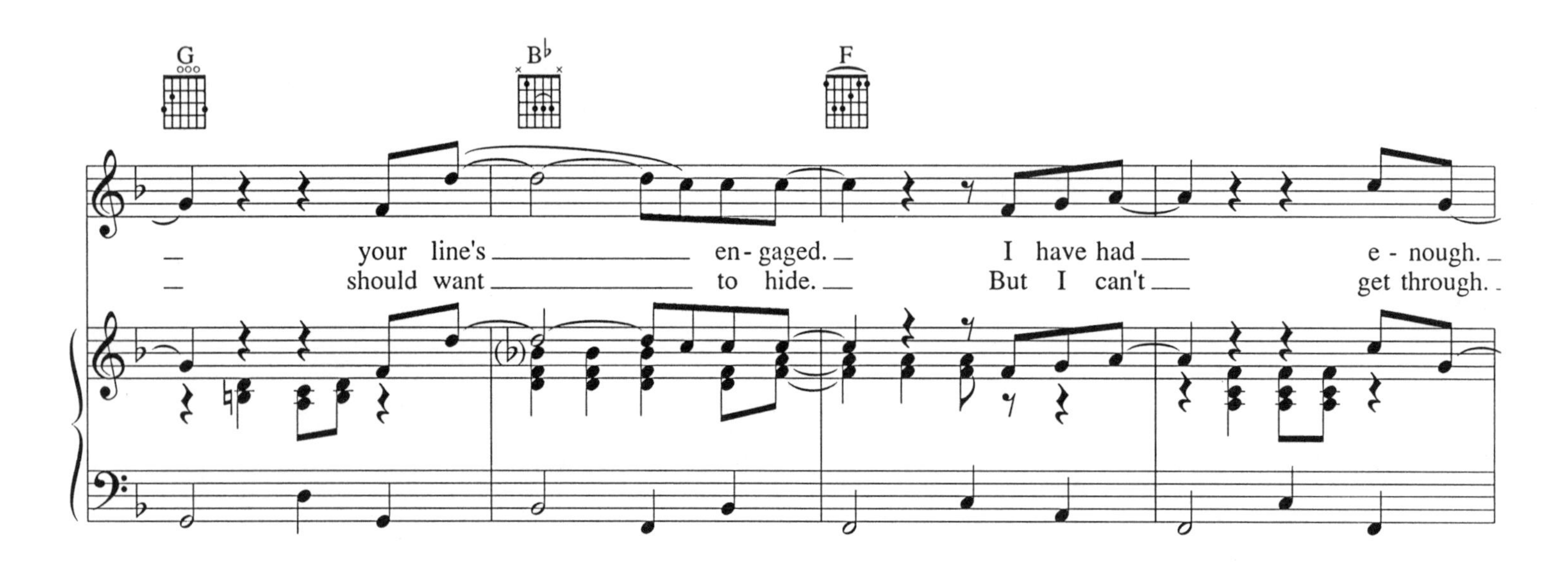

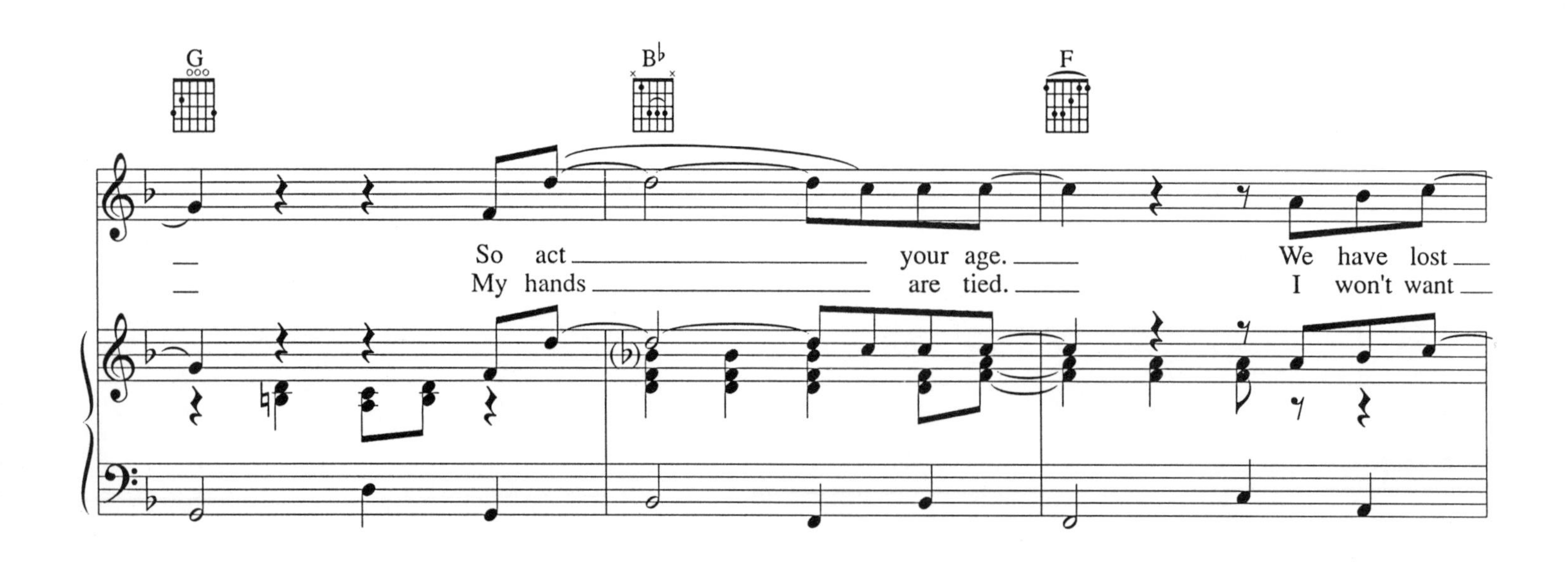

F7
B♭
B♭m
F
the time
that was so hard
to find;
And I will
to stay,
I don't have much
to say;
But I can
G
B♭
F
C7
D°
F
lose
my mind
if you won't
see me,
turn
a - way
and you won't
see me,
B♭
F
1
C7
D°
F
2
C7
D°
F
you won't
see me.
2. I don't know
you won't
see me.
Gm
B♭m6
B♭m6/C
F
Time af - ter time
you re - fuse
to ev - en lis - ten.

G7
C7sus
C7
I wouldn't mind if I knew what I was missing. 3. Though the days
F
G
B♭
F
are few, they're filled with tears; And since I
G
B♭
F
lost you it feels like years. Yes, it seems
F7
B♭
B♭m
F
so long girl, since you've been gone, And I just

G
1 B♭
F
C7
D°
F
can't go on if you won't see me,
B♭
F
C7
D°
F
2 B♭
F
you won't see me.
you won't see me.
C7
D°
F
B♭
F
C7
D°
F
You won't see me.
F
G7
B♭
F
Repeat and Fade
Oo la la la Oo la la la.

NORWEGIAN WOOD

Words & Music by John Lennon & Paul McCartney.

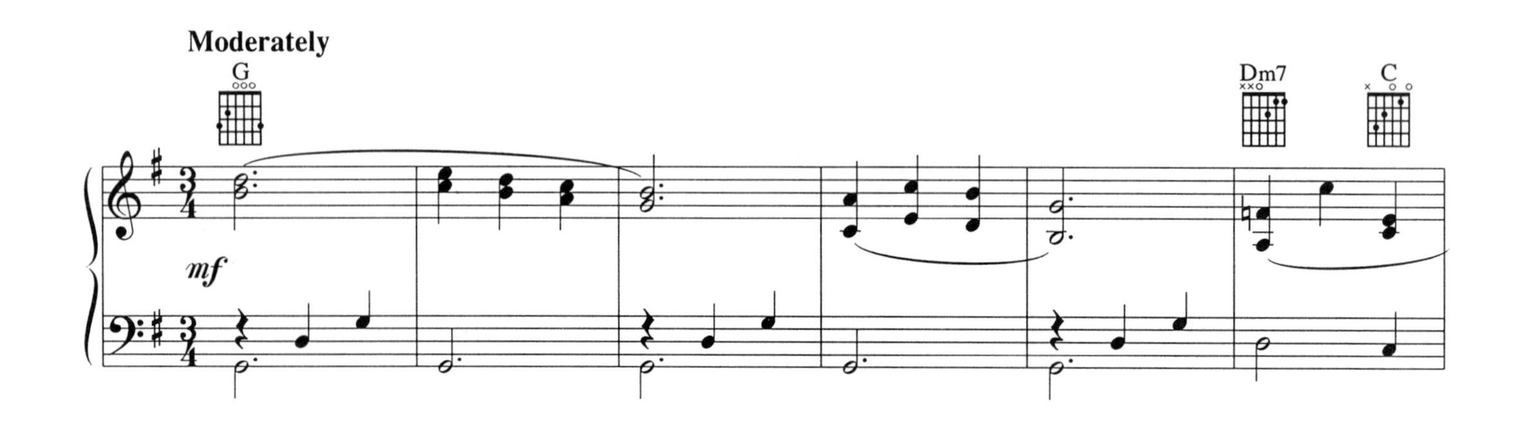

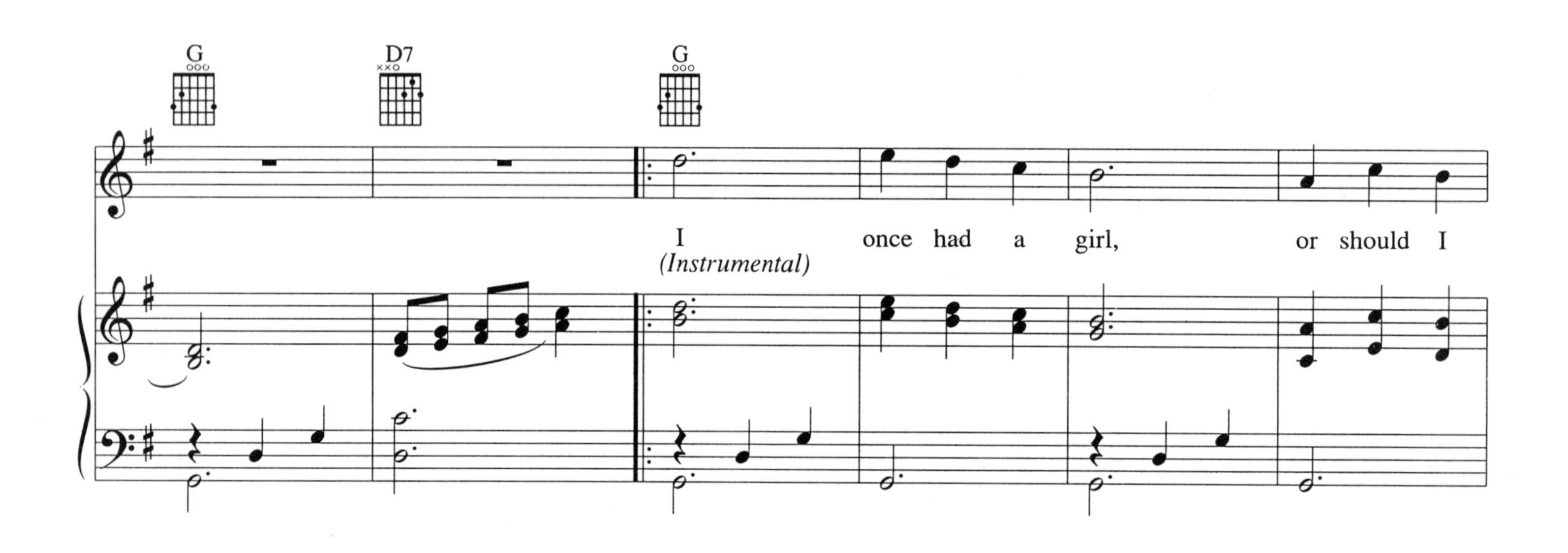

Dm7
C
G
room, Is - n't it good Nor - we - gian Wood?
1. She
2. She
Gm
C
asked me to stay and she told me to sit an - y - where,
told me she worked in the morn - ing and start - ed to laugh,
Gm
So I looked a - round and I no - ticed there
I told her I did - n't and crawled off to
Am7
D7
G
was - n't a chair. I
sleep in the bath. And
13

Dm7
C
G
sat on a rug, bid - ing my time, drink - ing her wine.
when I a - woke I was a - lone, This bird had flown.
G
We talked un - til two and then she said
So I lit a fire, is - n't it good
Dm7
C
1
G
2
G
"It's time for bed". Wood.
Nor - we - gian
Dm7
C
G
rit.

NOWHERE MAN

Words & Music by John Lennon & Paul McCartney.

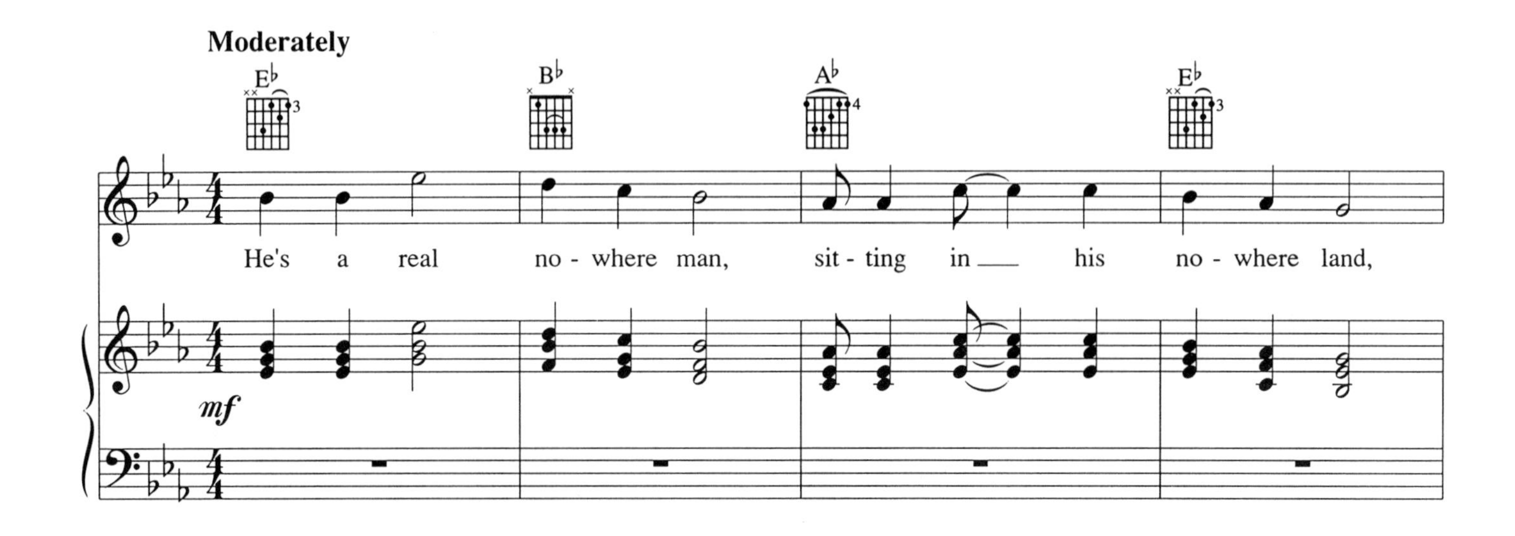

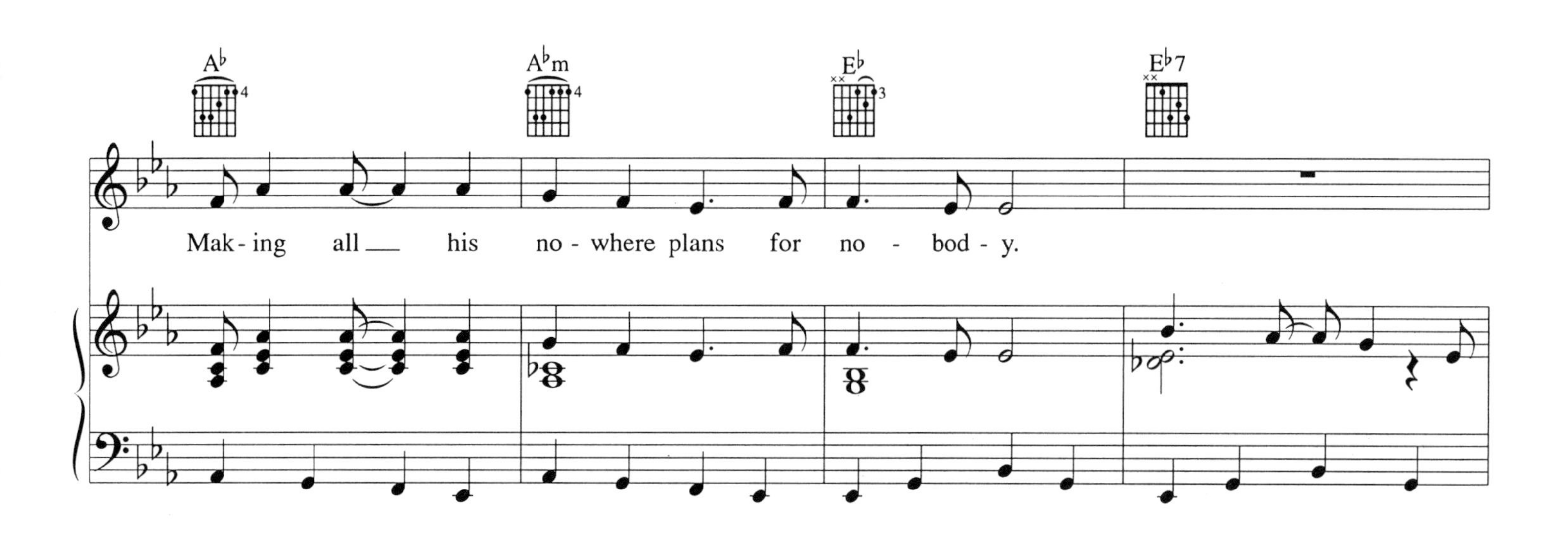

A♭
A♭m
E♭
is - n't he a bit like you and me?
no - where man, can you see me at all?
No - where man,
No - where man,
Gm
A♭
Gm
please lis - ten: You don't know what you're
don't wor - ry: Take your time, don't
please lis - ten: You don't know what you're
A♭
Gm
Fm7
miss - ing. No - where man, The world is
hur - ry. Leave it all 'Till some - bod - y else
miss - ing. No - where man, The world is
B♭
E♭
B♭
at your com - mand.
lends you a hand.
at your com - mand.
(Instrumental)
Does - n't have a point of view,
He's a real no - where man,

A♭
E♭
To Coda
A♭
A♭m
knows not where he's go - ing to
sit - ting in his no - where land,
Is - n't he a bit like you and
1 E♭
2 E♭
D.S. al Coda
me?
me?
No - where man,
Coda
A♭
A♭m
E♭
Mak - ing all his no - where plans for no - bod - y,
A♭
A♭m
E♭
Mak - ing all his no - where plans for no - bod - y.

THINK FOR YOURSELF

Words & Music by George Harrison

B♭
C
G
a - bout the good things that we can have if we close
I know your mind's made up, you're gon - na cause more mis -
and you've got time to rec - ti - fy all the things that

Am
C7
our eyes.
- er - y.
you should.
Do what you want to do, and

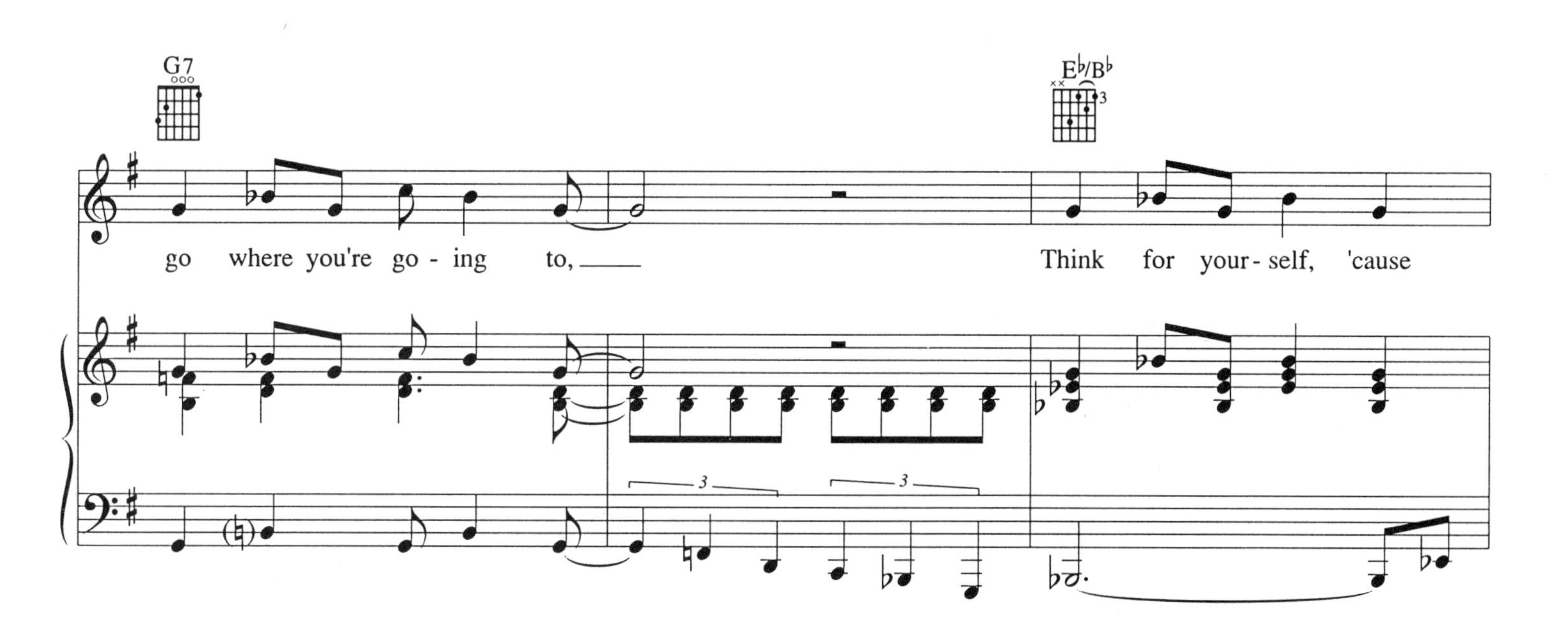
G7
E♭/B♭
go where you're go - ing to,
Think for your - self, 'cause

D7
To Coda
1.2
G
I won't be there with you.
3
G
D.S. al Coda
you.
Coda
C7
G
E♭/B♭
you.
Think for your-self, 'cause
D7
C7
G
I won't be there with you.

THE WORD

Words & Music by John Lennon & Paul McCartney.

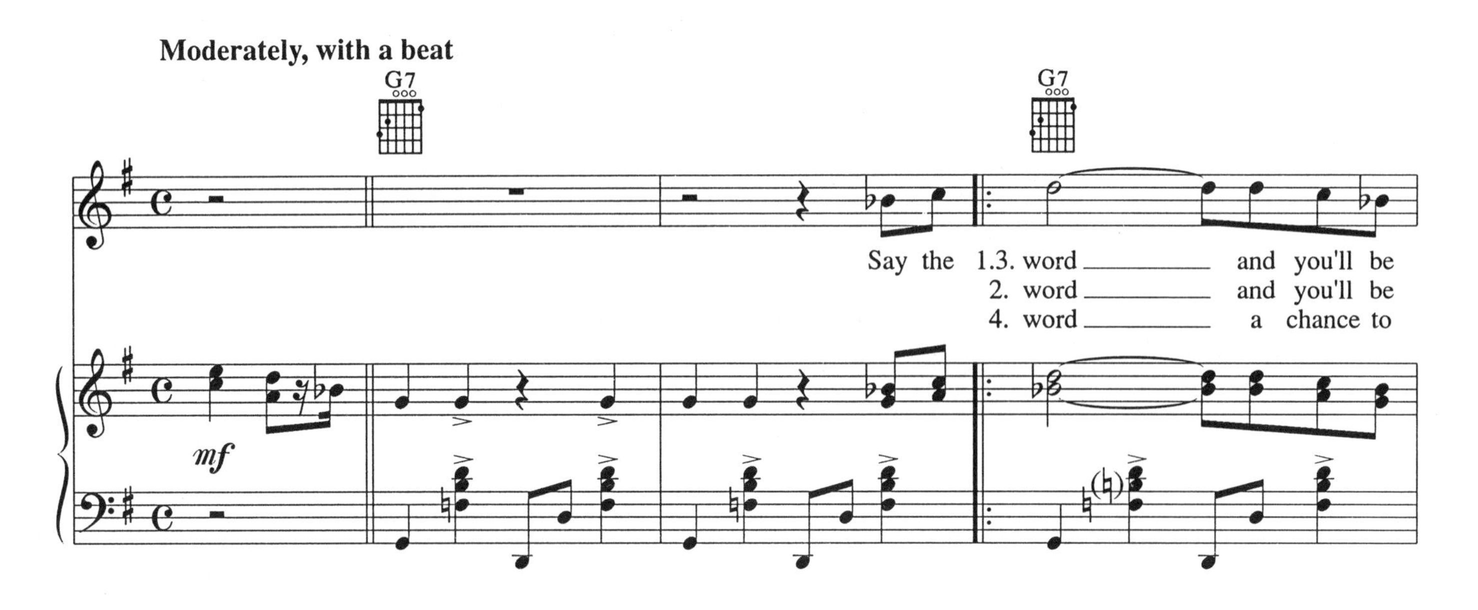

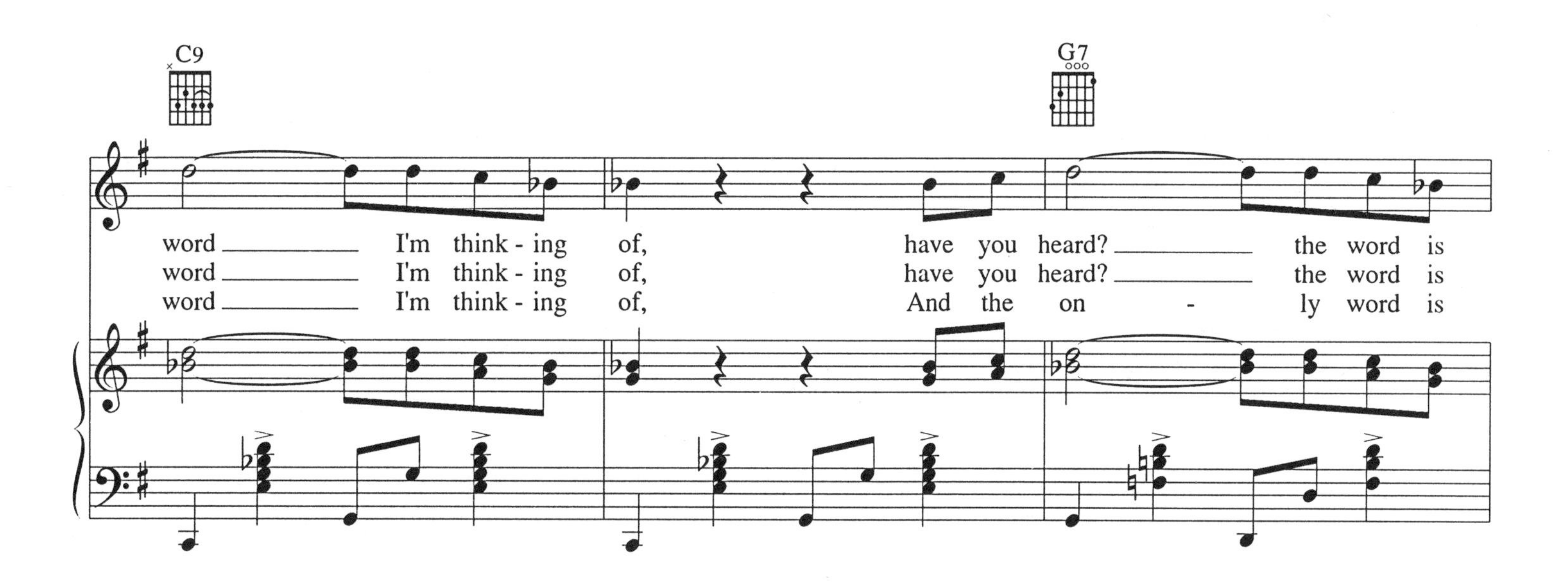

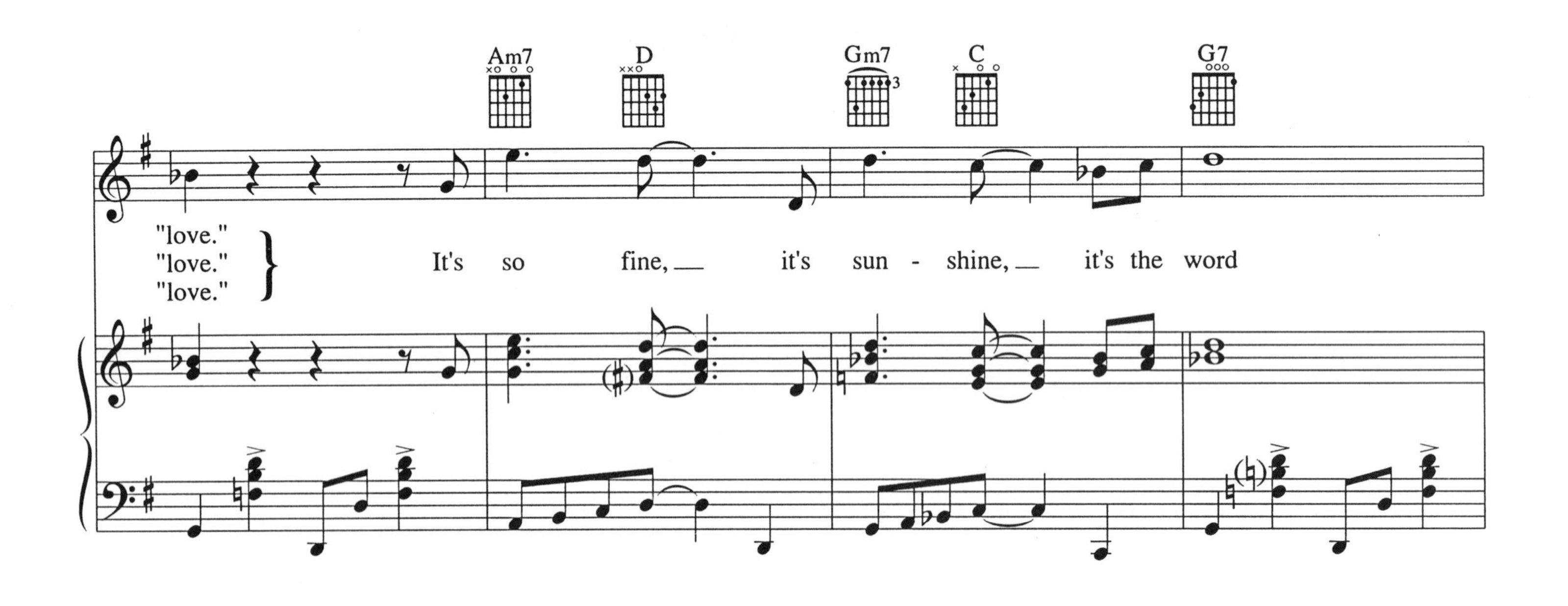
Am7
D
Gm7
C
G7
"love."
"love."
"love."
It's so fine, it's sun - shine, it's the word

1.2.3
G
F
"love."
1. In the be - gin - ning I mis - un - der - stood,
2. Ev - 'ry - where I go I hear it said,
3. Now that I know what I feel must be right,

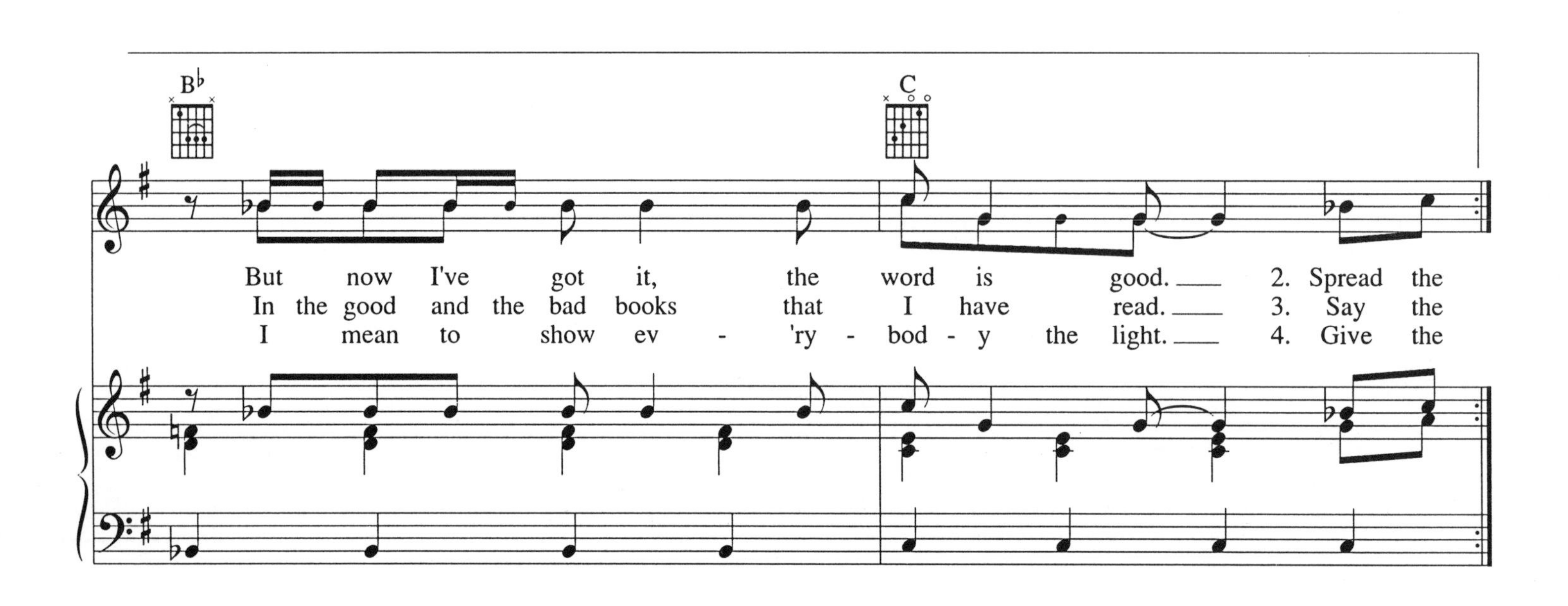
B♭
C
But now I've got it, the word is good. 2. Spread the
In the good and the bad books that I have read. 3. Say the
I mean to show ev - 'ry - bod - y the light. 4. Give the

4
G7
"love." Say the word "love." Say the
C9
G7
word "love." Say the word "love." Say the
Gm
D+
B♭/C
C9
G7
word "love."
Gm
F/G
Gm7
C/G
G

MICHELLE

Words & Music by John Lennon & Paul McCartney.

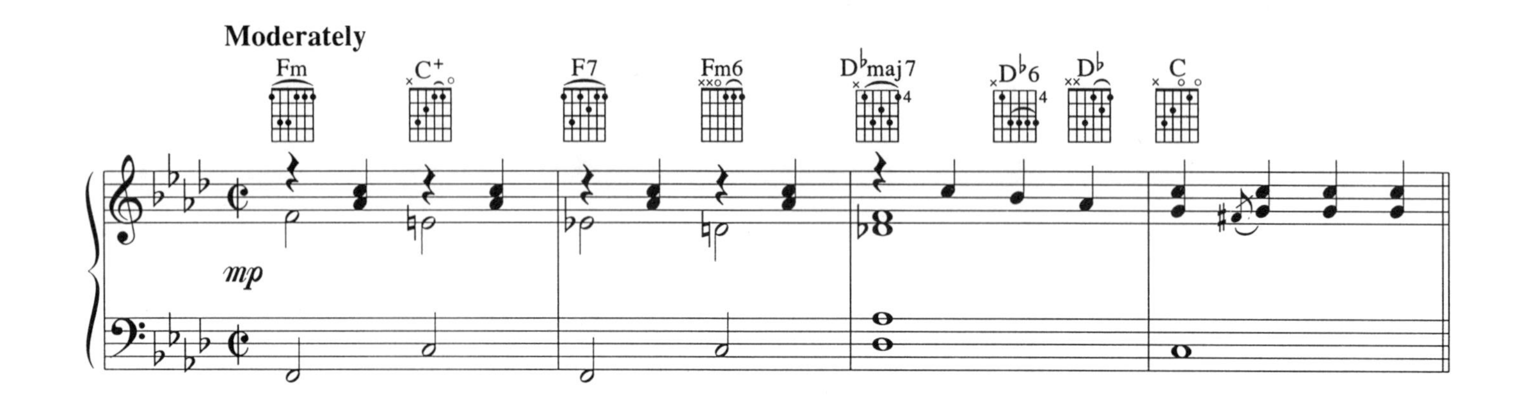

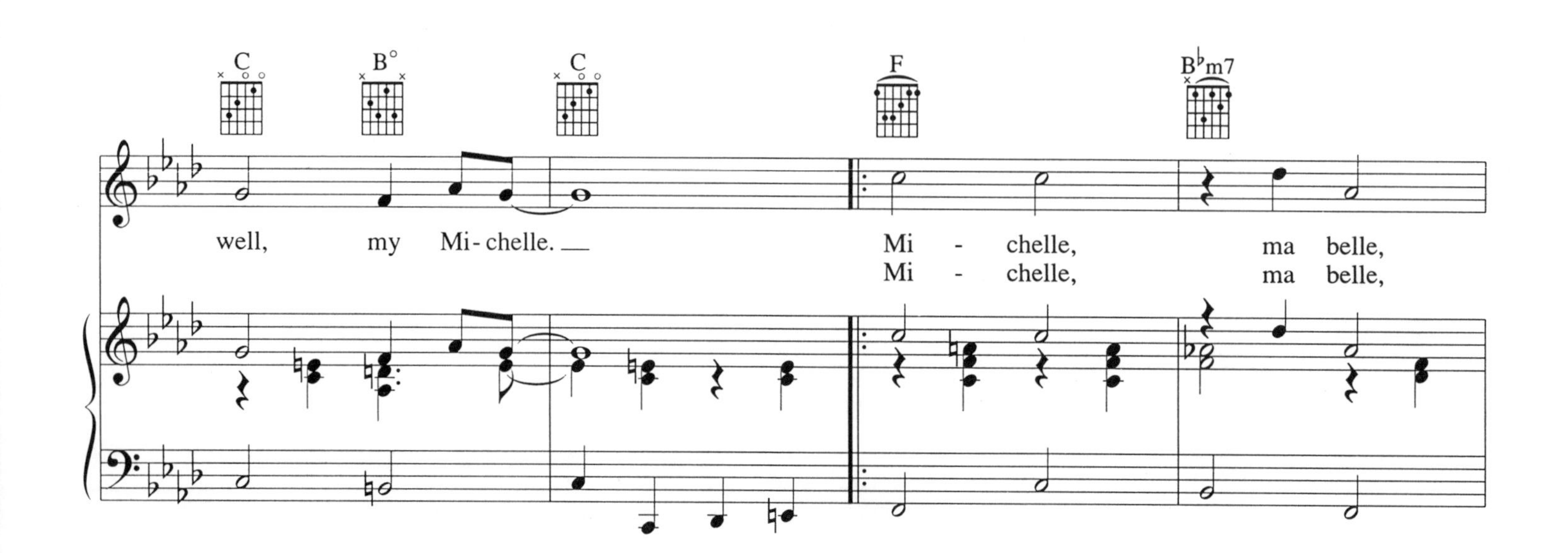

E♭ D° C B° C
sont les mots qui vont très bien en - semble, très bien en - semble. I
sont les mots qui vont très bien en - semble, très bien en - semble. I
Fm A♭7sus D♭
love you, I love you, I love you; That's all I want to say.
need to, I need to, I need to; I need to make you see.
C7sus Fm C+ Fm7 Fm6
Un - til I find a way, I will say the on - ly words I know that
Oh, what you mean to me un - til I do, I'm hop - ing you will
D♭maj7/F C C F
you'll un - der - stand. mean. I love you.
know what I

B♭m7 E♭ D° C B° C
I
(R.H.)
Fm A♭7sus
want you, I want you, I want you, I think you know by
D♭ C7sus Fm C+
now, I'll get to you some - how. Un - til I do, I'm
Fm7 Fm6 D♭maj7/F C F B♭m7
tell - ing you, so you'll un - der - stand: Mi - chelle, ma belle,

E♭
D°
C
B°
C
sont les mots qui vont très bien en - semble, très bien en - semble. And I will
Fm
C7
Fm7
Fm6
D♭/F
C
say the on - ly words I know that you'll un - der - stand, my Mi -
F
B♭m7
E♭
D°
- chelle.
C
B°
C
F
Repeat and Fade

WHAT GOES ON

Words & Music by John Lennon, Paul McCartney & Richard Starkey.

E♭
You are tear - ing me a - part
A♭7
When you treat me so un - kind.
B♭sus
B♭7
To Coda
last time
What goes on in your mind?
E♭
E♭
1. The oth - er day I
2. I met you in the
(3) used to think of

A♭m
saw you as I walked a - long the road. But
morn - ing wait - ing for the tides of time. But
no - one else, but you were just the same. You

E♭
A♭m
when I saw you with him, I could feel my fu - ture fold.
now the tide is turn - ing, I can see that I was blind.
did - n't e - ven think of me as some - one with a name.

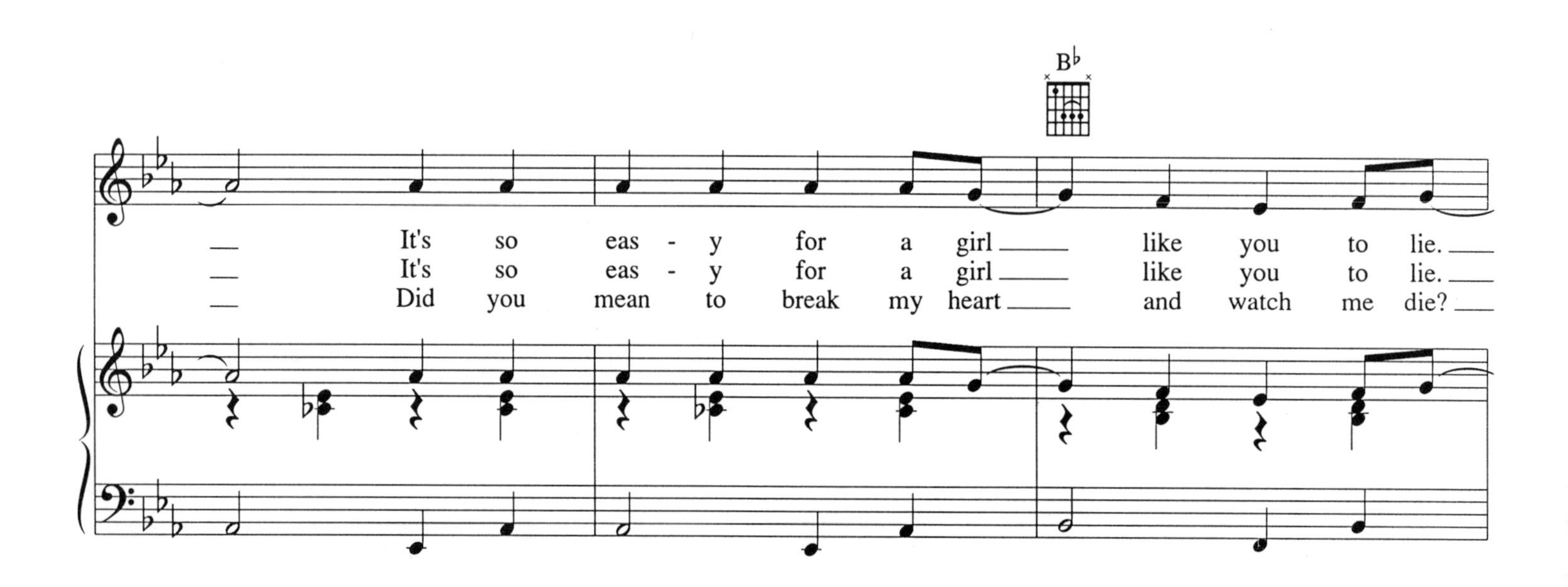
B♭
It's so eas - y for a girl like you to lie.
It's so eas - y for a girl like you to lie.
Did you mean to break my heart and watch me die?

E♭
B♭7
Tell me why.
Tell me why.
Tell me why.
1.3
2
What goes on
What goes on
in your heart?
A♭

A♭7
B♭7
E♭7
D.S. al Coda
3. I
Coda
E♭
E♭7
E♭
Tacet
E♭

GIRL

Words & Music by John Lennon and Paul McCartney.

E♭
Gm/D
Fm/C
B♭7
Girl,
Girl,
Girl.
Fm
B♭7
2. When I
She's the kind of girl who puts you
L.H.
C
Fm
down when friends are there, you feel a fool.
When you say she's look - ing good, she acts as if it's un - der-stood, she's cool, ooh,

A♭
E♭
Gm/D
Fm/C
B♭7
ooh,
ooh,
Girl,
E♭
Gm/D
Fm/C
B♭7
D.S. al Coda
Girl,
Girl,
3. Was she
Coda
E♭
Gm/D
Girl,
Fm/C
B♭7
E♭
Gm/D
Fm/C
B♭7
Girl.
Cm
G7
Cm
Fm
E♭
G7
(Instrumental)
Repeat & Fade

I'M LOOKING THROUGH YOU

Words & Music by John Lennon and Paul McCartney.

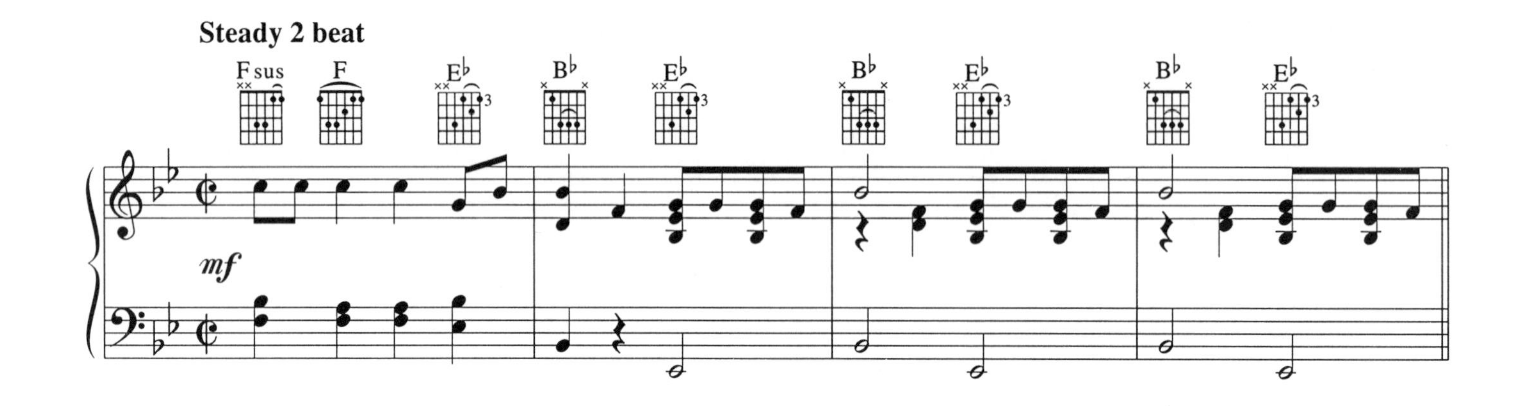

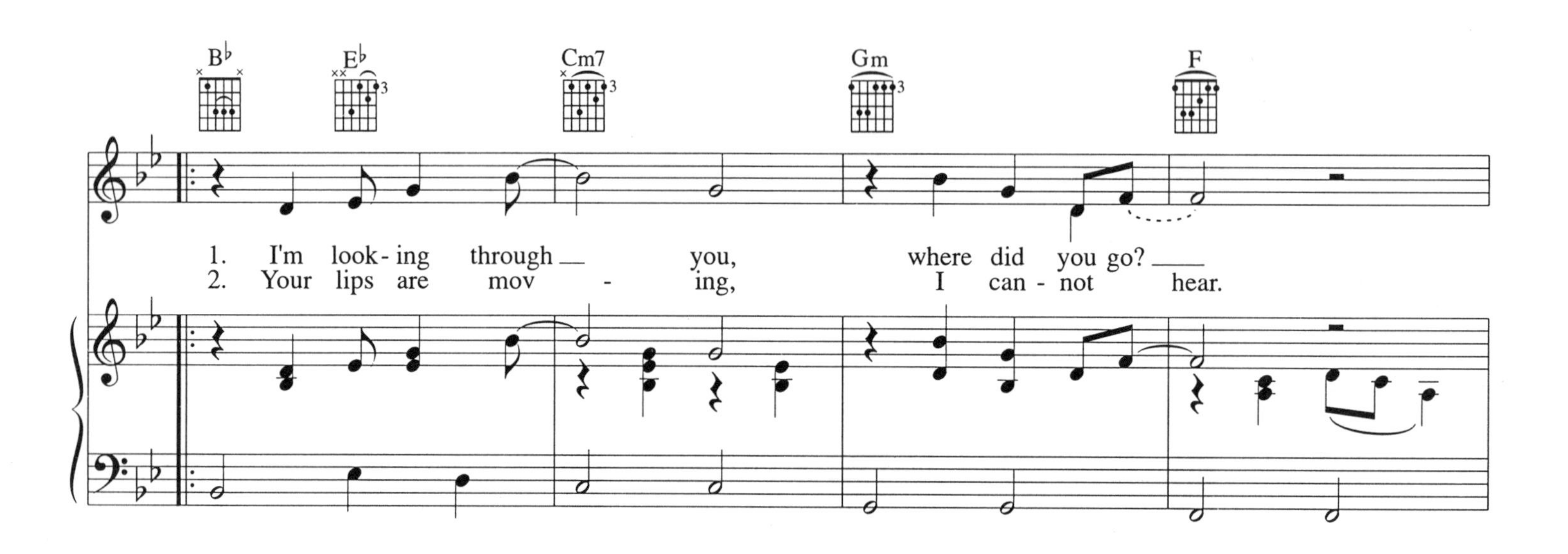

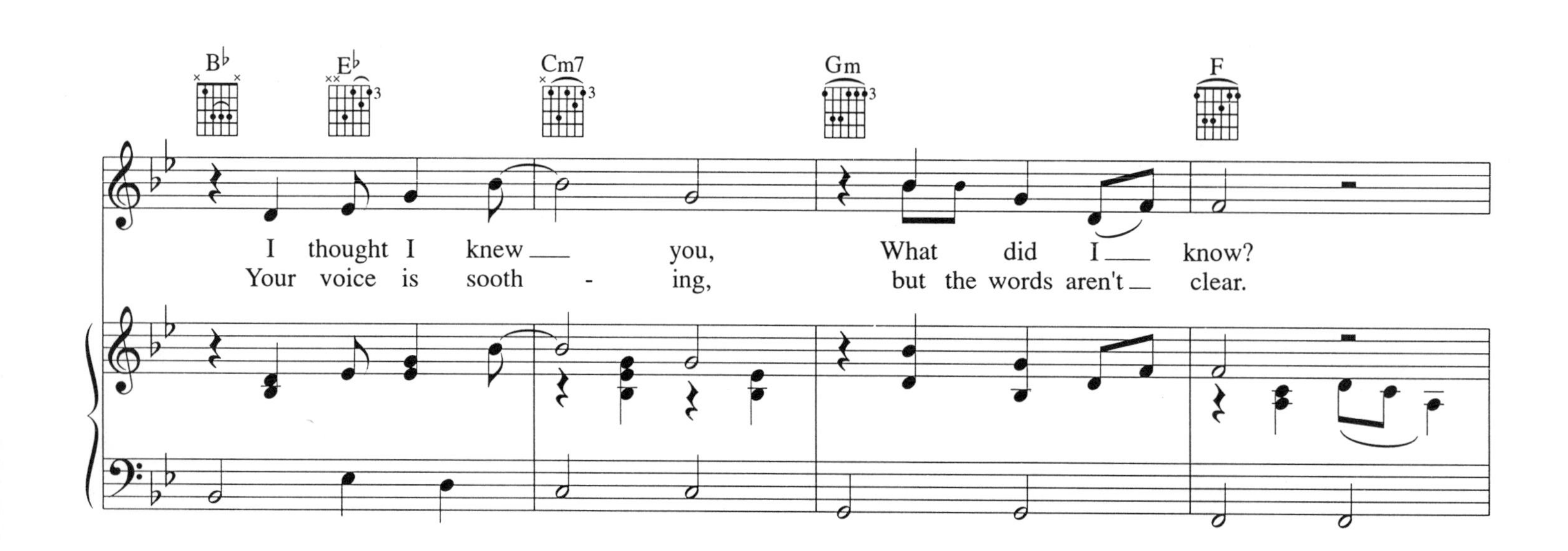

Gm
F
Cm
B♭
E♭
F
You don't look dif - f'rent, but you have changed;
You don't sound dif - f'rent, I've learned the game;
B♭
E♭
Cm7
E♭7
B♭
E♭
I'm look- ing through you, you're not the same.
B♭
E♭
B♭
E♭
B♭
E♭
E♭
B♭
Why, tell me why did you not treat me right?

E♭
Fsus
F
Love has a nas - ty hab - it of dis - ap - pear - ing o - ver - night.
B♭
E♭
Cm7
Gm
F
3. You're think - ing of me, the same old way;
4. I'm look - ing through you, where did you go?
B♭
E♭
Cm7
Gm
F
You were a - bove me, but not to - day.
I thought I knew you, what did I know?
Gm
F
Cm
B♭
E♭
F
The on - ly dif - f'rence is you're down there;
You don't look dif - f'rent, but you have changed;

B♭
E♭
Cm7
E♭7
I'm look - ing through you and you're no - where.
I'm look - ing through you, you're not the same.
Yeah! Well, ba - by you've changed.
Repeat and Fade
Ah, I'm look - ing through you.

IN MY LIFE

Words & Music by John Lennon and Paul McCartney.

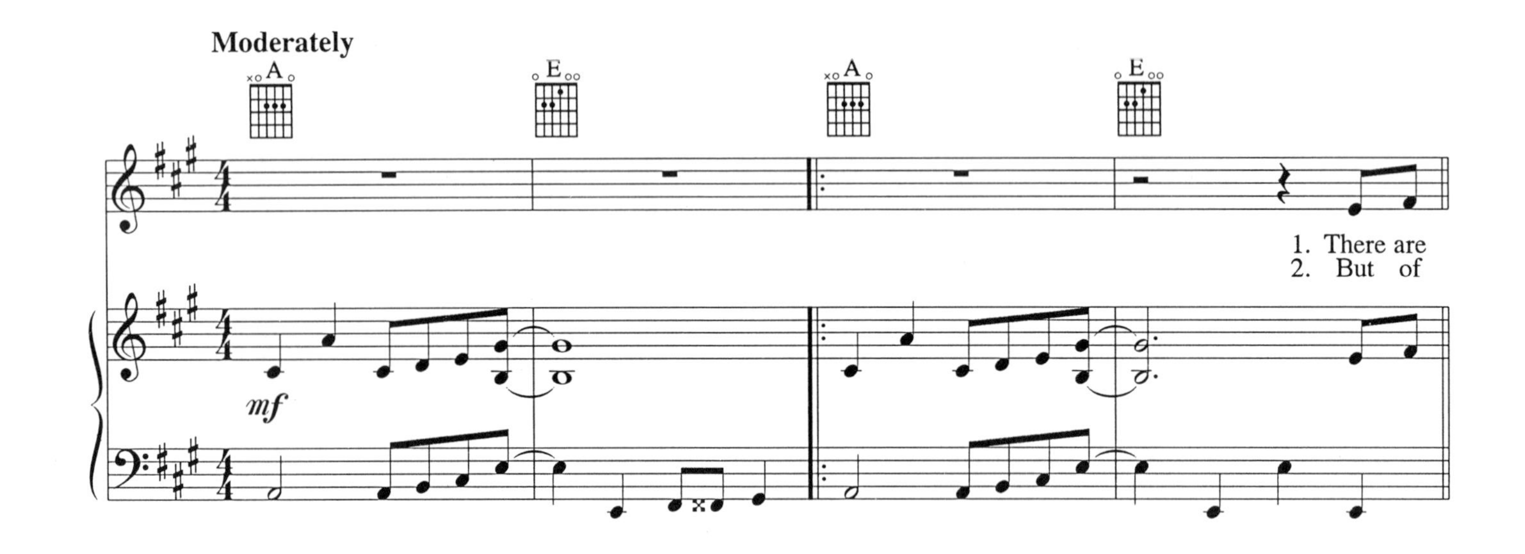

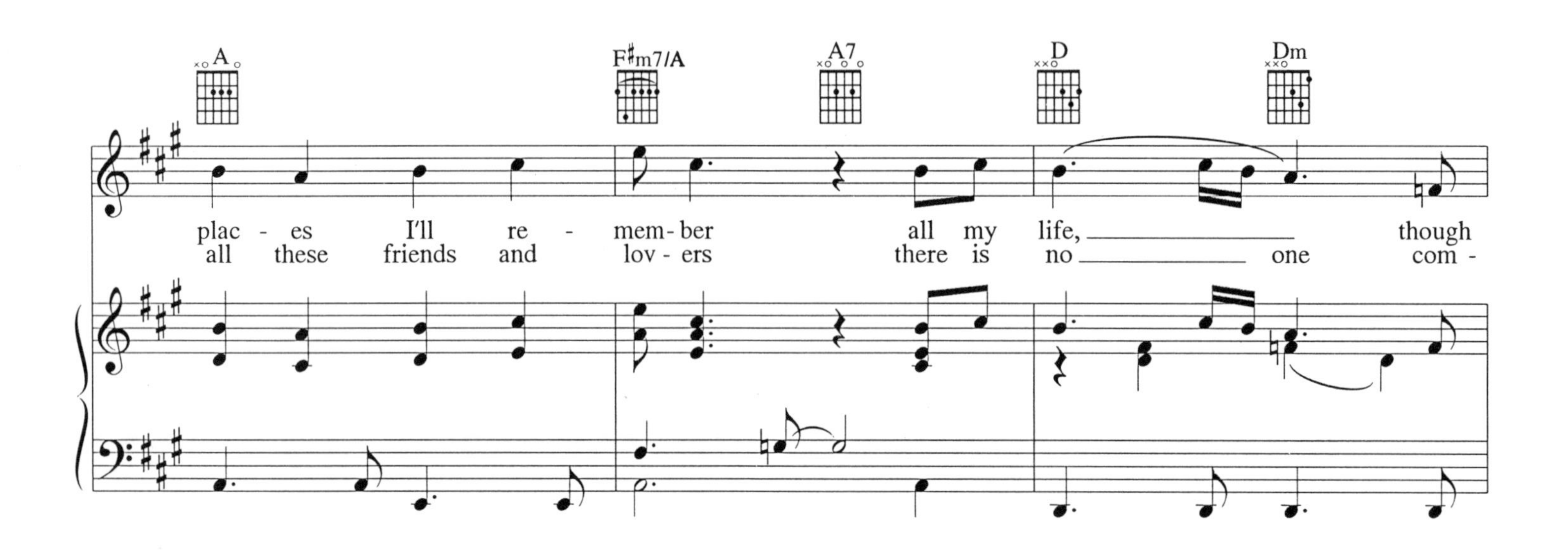

D
Dm
A
F♯m7
gone and some re-main. All these (1) plac - es had their
think of love as some-thing new. Tho' I (2,3) know I'll nev-er lose af -

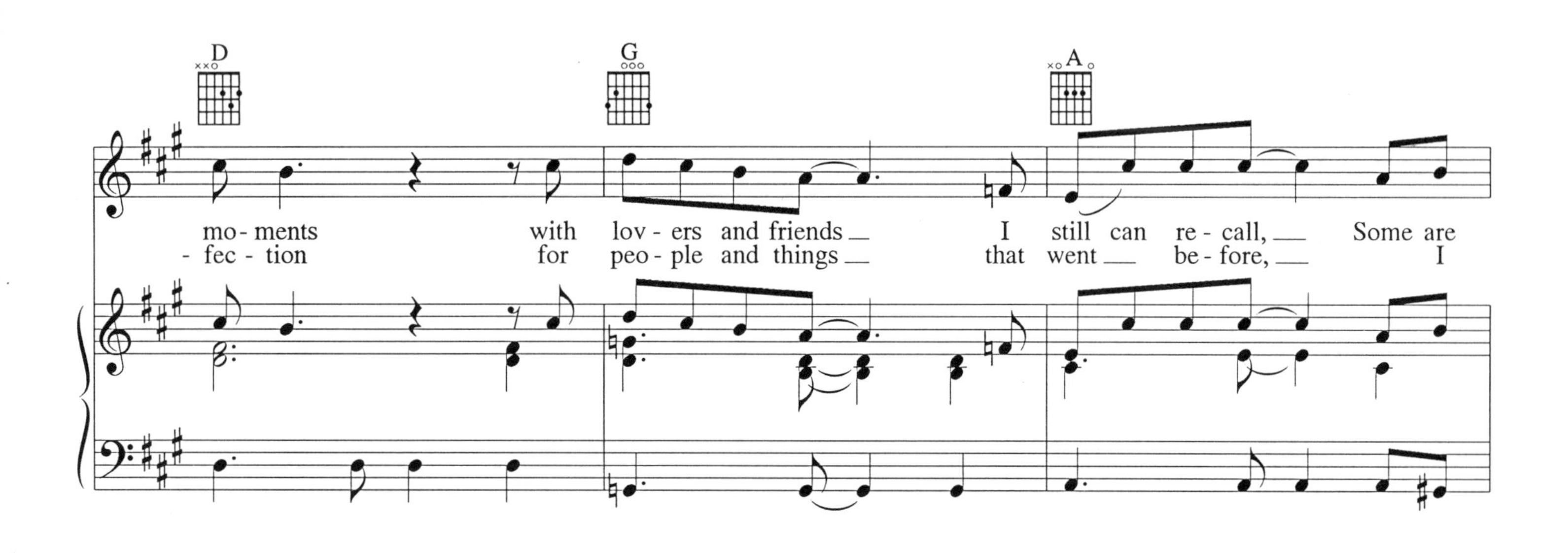
D
G
A
mo-ments with lov-ers and friends I still can re-call, Some are
- fec-tion for peo-ple and things that went be-fore, I

F♯m
B7
Dm
dead and some are liv - ing; in my life I've
know I'll of-ten stop and think a - bout them, in my life I

A
To Coda
A
E
F♯m
A7
loved them all.
love you more.
D
Dm
1 A
2 A
D.S. al Coda
3. Tho' I
Coda
A
E
Dm
in my life I
Slower
Tacet
A
E
E7
A
love you more.
a tempo

IF I NEEDED SOMEONE

Words & Music by George Harrison.

F7
B♭m
- er day, then it might not have been like this,
E♭m
F7
B♭m
But you see now I'm too much in love.
E♭
A♭
Carve your num - ber on my wall and may -
G♭/A♭
- be you will get a call from me,

A♭
To Coda
If I need - ed some - one.
A♭
Ah
Ah
Ah
G♭/A♭
A♭
D.S. al Coda
Ah
Coda
A♭
Ah
Ah.

WAIT

Words & Music by John Lennon and Paul McCartney.

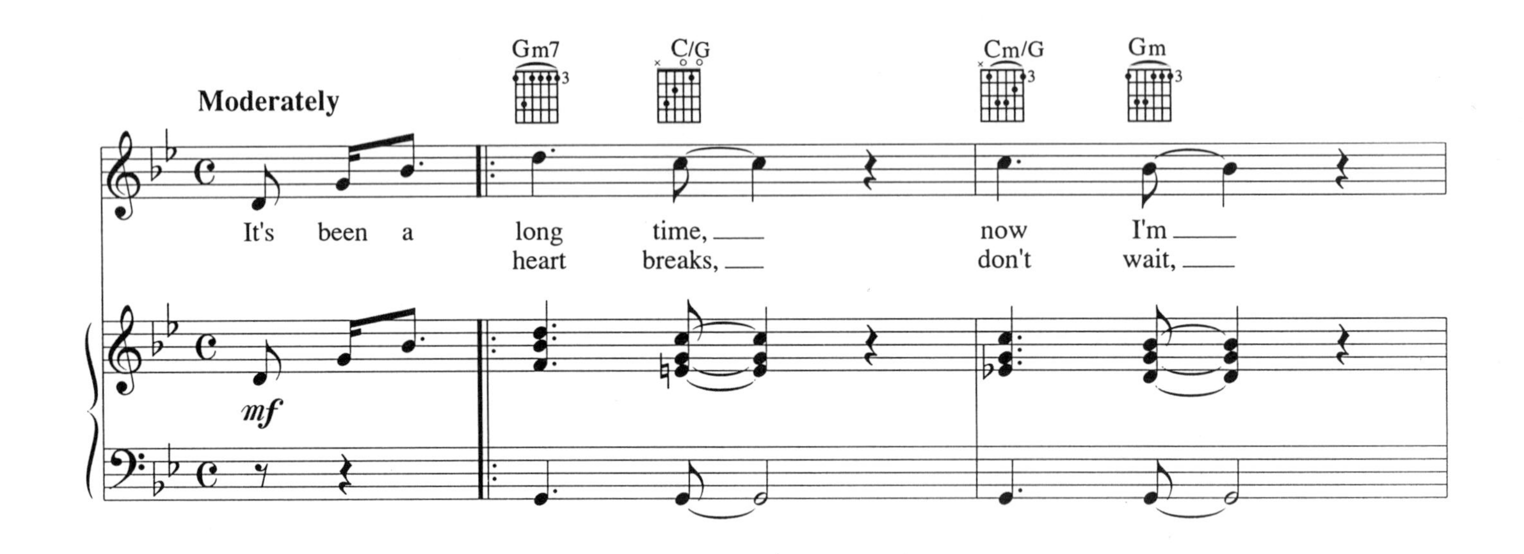

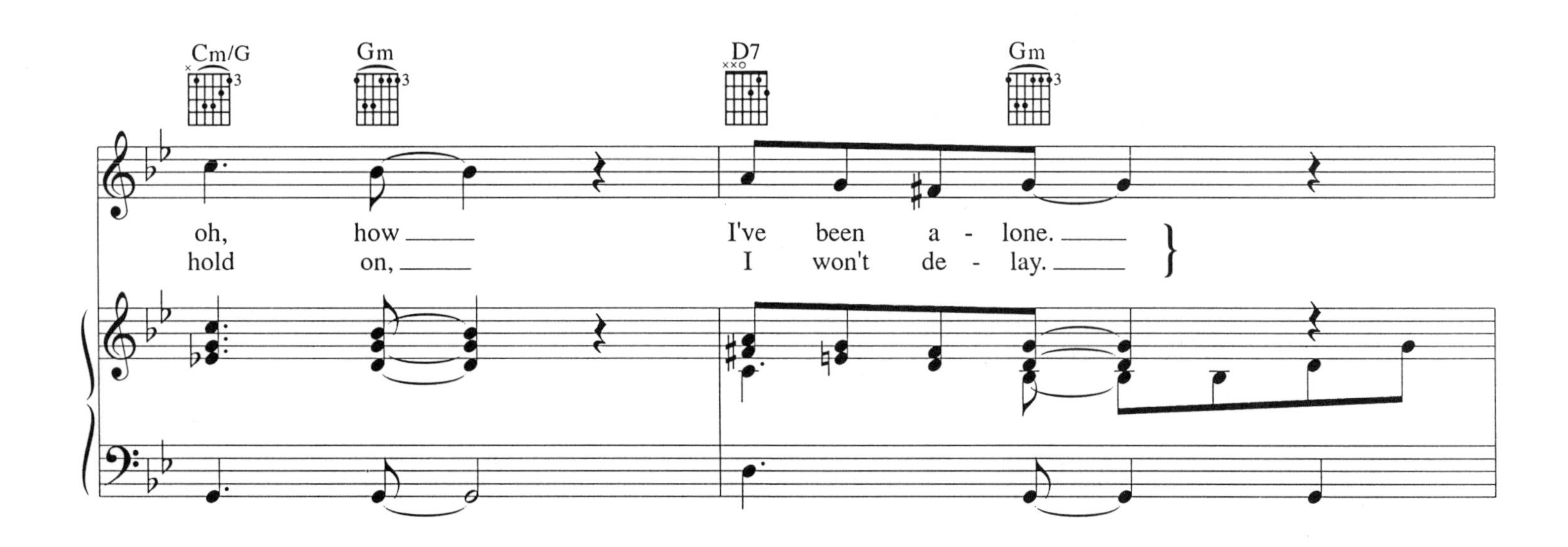

B♭
E♭maj7
B♭
E♭maj7
B♭
E♭maj7
Wait 'til I come back to your side, we'll for -
B♭
D7
1 Gm
2 Gm
- get the tears we cried; But if your I feel as
Cm
F
though you ought to know that I've been
B♭
Gm
Cm
good, as good as I can be. And if you do, I'll trust in

F
B♭
Gm
D7
you and know that you will wait for me.
It's been a
But if your
Gm7
C/G
Cm/G
Gm
D7
Gm
long time, now I'm com - ing back home. I've been a -
heart breaks, don't wait, turn me a - way. And if your
Gm7
C/G
Cm/G
Gm
- way now, oh, how
heart's strong, hold on,
D7
Gm
B♭
E♭maj7
I've been a - lone.
I won't de - lay.
Wait 'til I

B♭ E♭maj7 B♭ E♭maj7 B♭ D7
come back to your side, we'll for - get the tears we cried;
1 Gm 2 Gm Gm7 C/G
I feel as It's been a long time,
Cm/G Gm D7 Gm Gm7 C/G
now I'm com - ing back home, I've been a - way now,
Cm/G Gm D7 Gm
oh how I've been a - lone.
rit.

RUN FOR YOUR LIFE

Words & Music by John Lennon & Paul McCartney.

D
You'd bet - ter keep your head lit - tle girl, or I
And I can't spend my whole life try - in' just to
Ba - by, I'm de - ter - mined and I'd
Bm
won't know where I am.
make you toe the line.
rath - er see you dead.
You'd bet - ter run for your life if you can,
E
Bm
E
lit - tle girl. Hide your head in the sand lit - tle girl,
Bm
G
F♯7
Bm
To Coda
Catch you with an - oth - er man, that's the end - a, lit - tle

1.3
Bm
D7
girl.
2
D7
2. Well, you girl.
3. I'd
D.S. al Coda
Coda
D7
girl.
Repeat and Fade
No, no, no.

The Beatles: Music Books In Print

The Best Of The Beatles: Book 1
NO18541

The Best Of The Beatles: Book 2
NO18558

The Best Of The Beatles: Book 3 Sgt. Pepper
NO18566

The Best Of The Beatles : Book 4
NO18608

The Best Of The Beatles: Book 5
NO18616

Beatles Big Note: Piano/Vocal Edition
NO17428

Beatles Big Note: Guitar Edition
NO17402

A Collection Of Beatles Oldies: Piano Vocal Edition
NO17659

A Collection Of Beatles Oldies: Guitar Edition
NO18004

The Beatles Complete: Piano/ Vocal/Easy Organ Edition
NO17162

The Beatles Complete (Revised)
Re-engraved, revised edition of 'The Beatles Complete'. For piano/organ/ vocal, complete with lyrics and guitar chord symbols. Includes every song composed and recorded by the group. 203 songs, plus 24-page appreciation by Ray Connolly, lavishly illustrated with rare photographs.
Piano/Organ/Vocal Edition
NO18160
Guitar/Vocal Edition
NO18145

The Beatles Bumper Songbook
Full piano/vocal arrangements of 100 songs made famous by the Fab Four. Includes 'All You Need Is Love', 'Yellow Submarine', 'Lucy In The Sky With Diamonds' and 'Hey Jude', all complete with lyrics. 256 pages in all.
NO17998

The Concise Beatles Complete
NO18244

The Beatles Complete: Chord Organ Edition
NO17667

The Beatles Complete: Guitar Edition
NO17303

The Beatles: A Hard Day's Night
NO90542

Beatles For Sale
NO17584

The Beatles: Help
NO90541

The Beatles: Highlights
NO18525

The Beatles: Let It Be
NO90536

The Beatles: Love Songs
NO17915

The Beatles: Magical Mystery Tour
NO17600

The Beatles 1962-1966
NO17931

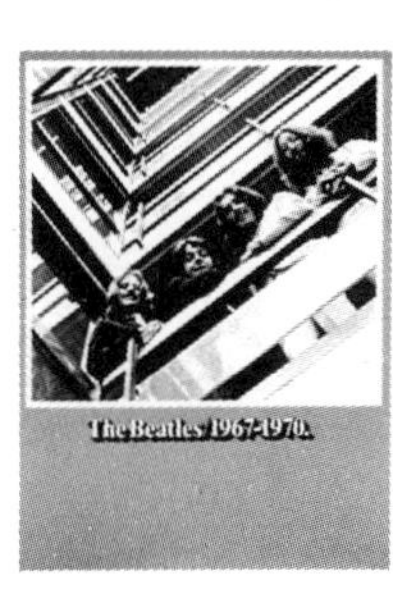

The Beatles 1967-70
NO17949

The Beatles: Revolver
NO90539

The Beatles Rock Score
Twelve numbers scored for groups. Perfect note-for-note transcriptions from the recordings for vocal and each instrument, in standard notation and guitar tablature. Includes drum line and lyrics.
NO18442

Rubber Soul
NO90540

The Singles Collection 1962-1970
NO17741

The 6 Chord Songbook
NO18418

The 6 Chord Songbook: Book 2
NO18517

20 Greatest Hits: Piano/Vocal Edition
NO18269

20 Greatest Hits: Easy Guitar
NO18277

White Album
NO90538

The Songs Of George Harrison
AM30990

The Great Songs Of George Harrison
AM37649

The Great Songs Of John Lennon
AM61854

KEYBOARD/PIANO SONGBOOKS

101 Beatles Songs For Buskers
Includes all their favourite songs in melody line arrangements, complete with lyrics and guitar chord boxes.
Piano/Organ Edition.
NO18392

Beatles Best for Keyboard
HD10029

The Complete Keyboard Player: The Beatles
NO18509

The Complete Piano Player Beatles
NO18806

Creative Keyboard Series: The Beatles
AM71911

Home Organist Library: Volume 9 Beatles Songs
NO18186

The Beatles. 100 Hits For All Keyboards
Special lay-flat, spiral-bound collection of favourite Beatles songs arranged for all keyboards – piano, electronic piano, organ and portable keyboards. With full lyrics.
NO18590

It's Easy To Play Beatles
NO17907

It's Easy To Play Beatles 2
NO90342

SFX-3: Beatles Hits
AM33093

SFX-16: Beatles Hits 2
AM39660

GUITAR

Beatles Guitar: Tablature
NO18798

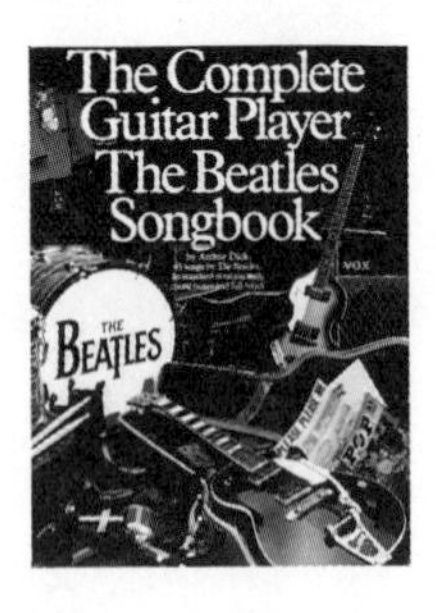

The Complete Guitar Player: The Beatles
NO18491

The Beatles For Classical Guitar
NO17444

The Beatles For Classical Guitar: Book 2
NO17782

Fingerpicking Beatles
AM30941

WIND INSTRUMENTS

Beatles For Recorder
NO18434

Greatest Hits For Harmonica
NO18673

Beatles: Themes And Variations: Clarinet
NO17873

Beatles: Themes And Variations: Flute
NO17865

Beatles: Themes And Variations: Trumpet
NO17881

Lennon & McCartney For Clarinet
NO17725

Lennon & McCartney For Clarinet
NO18764

Lennon & McCartney For Flute
NO18756

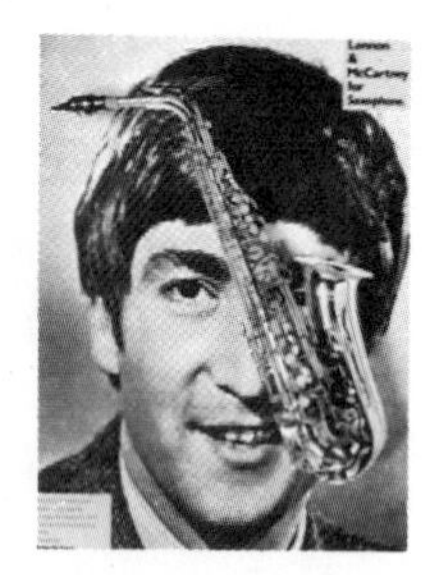

Lennon & McCartney For Saxophone
NO18772

Lennon & McCartney For Trumpet
NO17733

Lennon & McCartney For Trumpet
NO18780

Lennon & McCartney 60 Greatest For Trumpet
NO18715

GERMAN EDITIONS

Beatles Für Die Blockflöte
MG13582

Die Beatles Für Klassische Gitarre: Band 1
MG13202

OMNIBUS PRESS

The Beatles Apart
PRP10083

The Beatles Book
OP43439

The Complete Beatles Lyrics
OP42027

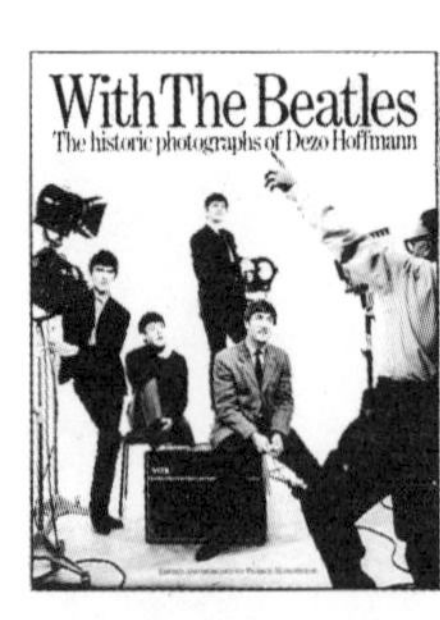

With The Beatles: The Historic Photographs Of Dezo Hoffmann
OP41961

Beatles: In Their Own Words
OP40419

Paul McCartney: In His Own Words
OP40047

Available from all good Music Shops.

In case of difficulty, please contact:
Music Sales Limited
Newmarket Road, Bury St. Edmunds, Suffolk IP33 3YB, England.
Telephone: 0284 702600. Fax: 0284 768301. Telex: 817845.